WORLD OF VOCABULARY

YELLOW

Sidney J. Rauch   Alfred B. Weinstein

Assisted by Carole Reynolds

GLOBE BOOK COMPANY, INC.

A Division of Simon & Schuster

New York/Cleveland/Toronto/Sydney/Tokyo/Singapore

D0259671

PHOTO CREDITS

Page 2, 5: Brian Lanker, from his book *I Dream A World*; 8: The MacNeil/Lehrer News Hour; 10, 13: New York *Daily News*; 18: Tony Costa/Outline; 21: John Barr/Gamma Liaison; 23: Smeal/Galella; 26, 29: Jolie Stahl; 31: Chester Higgins, Jr./NYT Pictures; 34: Barry Talesnick/Retna Ltd.; 37, 39: Outline; 42, 45, 47, 58, 61, 63: The Bettmann Archive; 50, 53, 55: The *Amsterdam News*; 66: Popperfoto; 69, 71: The Granger Collection; 74, 77, 79: © 1989 Warner Bros. Inc. All rights reserved; 82, 85: Bernie Liebler; 87: John Zimmerman; 90, 95: Ron Galella; 93: Globe Photos; 98, 101, 103, 114, 117, 119: Wide World Photos; 106, 109, 112: New York City Opera Co.

World of Vocabulary, Yellow Level, Second Edition
Sidney J. Rauch   Alfred B. Weinstein

Copyright © 1991 by Globe Book Company, Inc., 190 Sylvan Avenue, Englewood Cliffs, New Jersey 07632. All rights reserved. No part of this book may be kept in an information storage or retrieval system, transmitted or reproduced in any form or by any means without the prior written permission of the publisher. Published simultaneously in Canada by Globe/Modern Curriculum Press.

ISBN 1-55675-358-6   Printed in the United States of America
                                                              10 9 8 7

SIDNEY J. RAUCH is Professor of Reading and Education at Hofstra University, and senior author of the World of Vocabulary series. He has been a visiting professor at numerous universities and is active as a lecturer and consultant. As a member of the College Proficiency Examination Committee of the New York State Education Department, he was involved in the certification of reading personnel. He has given in-service courses and has served as consultant to over thirty school districts in New York, Florida, North Carolina, South Carolina, and the U.S. Virgin Islands. Dr. Rauch was named Reading Educator of the Year for 1985 by the New York State Reading Association.

As coauthor and editor, his texts include: A Need to Read series, *Handbook for the Volunteer Tutor (Second Edition), Guiding the Reading Program, Cloze Thinking, Mastering Reading Skills,* and *Corrective Reading in the High School Classroom.* He is author of the Barnaby Brown books, a children's series. Dr. Rauch's many articles have appeared in *The Reading Teacher, Journal of Reading, Reading World,* and conference proceedings of the International Reading Association.

ALFRED B. WEINSTEIN is the former principal of Myra S. Barnes Intermediate School (Staten Island, N.Y.) Dr. Weinstein has taught extensively at the secondary school level, and he has served as an elementary school principal and assistant principal. He has been a reading clinician and instructor at Hofstra University Reading Center. At Queens College he gave courses in reading improvement, and at Brooklyn College he taught in the graduate teacher education program. Dr. Weinstein has also taught reading for the New York City Board of Education's in-service teacher training program. He was head of Unit 1 of the Board of Examiners and supervised the licensing of teachers, supervisors, administrators, psychologists, and social workers for the New York City Board of Education. He is vice-president of the Council of Supervisors and Administrators of Local 1 of the AFL-CIO. Dr. Weinstein has been listed in *Who's Who in the East* since 1982.

Dr. Weinstein is a contributor to the *Handbook for the Volunteer Tutor* and one of the authors of *Achieving Reading Skills.* With Dr. Rauch, he is coauthor of *Mastering Reading Skills.*

CONTENTS ▰▰▰▰▰▰▰▰▰▰▰▰▰▰▰▰▰▰▰

WOMAN IN THE NEWS

Perhaps you have seen Charlayne Hunter-Gault on television. She has been an important part of the *MacNeil/Lehrer Newshour* since 1978. Before that she was a reporter for *The New York Times*. She has received many awards for reporting the news.

In 1961, Charlayne Hunter-Gault *was* the news. She was the first black female student to go to the University of Georgia. It was a difficult time for Charlayne. People yelled at her. They called her names. One night, a brick crashed through her window. She remembers thinking, "Wow! There is a riot in my room." But she would not let herself be afraid.

Charlayne brings the same strength to her job as a reporter. She had faced problems both as an African American and as a woman. But she does not let anything interfere with her work. Charlayne has always been confident . She knows she is a good reporter.

Charlayne Hunter-Gault believes it is a reporter's job to tell people the truth. She speaks out against injustice in the United States and around the world. Charlayne says, "If people are informed , they will do the right thing."

MAKE A LIST

▶ **There are eight vocabulary words in this lesson. In the story, they are boxed in color. Copy the vocabulary words here.**

1. reporter
2. university
3. difficult
4. riot
5. interfere
6. confident
7. injustice
8. informed

▶ Here are the eight words you copied on the previous page. Write then in alphabetical order in the blank spaces below.

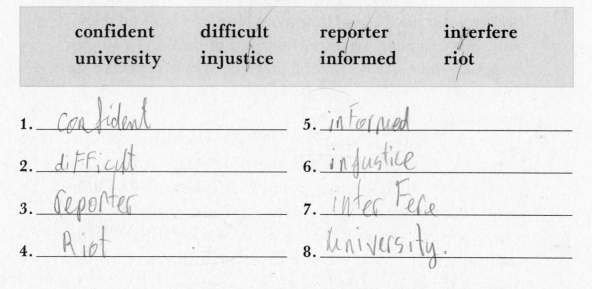

confident	difficult	reporter	interfere
university	injustice	informed	riot

1. _confident_
2. _difficult_
3. _reporter_
4. _Riot_

5. _informed_
6. _injustice_
7. _interfere_
8. _university._

WHAT DO THE WORDS MEAN?

▶ Here are some meanings for the eight vocabulary words in this lesson. Four words have been written beside their meanings. Write the other four words next to their meanings.

1. _cofident_ having faith or trust in oneself

2. _reporter_ someone who writes about or tells about the news

3. _injustice_ something that harms the rights of others

4. _Difficult_ not easy; hard

5. _informed_ given information; told

6. _university_ a school of higher learning; college

7. _riot_ a wild disturbance caused by a group of people

8. _interfere_ to get in the way of

▶ Look at the picture. What words come into your mind? Write them on the blank lines below. To help you get started, here are two good words:

1. _____smart_____   5. _aving faith in her self._

2. _____collar_____   6. _happy._____

3. _____Sirius_____   7. _____

4. ____nice lady_____   8. _____

▶ A **synonym** is a word that means the same, or nearly the same, as another word. *Happy* and *glad* are synonyms.

▶ **The column on the left contains the eight key words used in the story. To the right of each key word are three other words or groups of words. Two of these are synonyms for the key word. Circle the synonyms.**

1. **difficult**   easy   (hard)   not easy

2. **interfere**   block   (interrupt)   interest

3. **riot**   (violence)   disturbance   playfulness

4. **university**   (school)   park   college

5. **reporter**   (writer)   news   newspaper
                                    gatherer

6. **confident**   (secure)   sure   uncertain

7. **informed**   told   (given   questioned
                                    information)

8. **injustice**   injury   (unfairness)   uniform

6

▶ In each of the following sentences there are words which need capital letters. Rewrite each sentence so the words are correctly capitalized. Remember that capital letters are used in the following places: first word in a sentence; names of people, cities, states, countries; days of the week; months of the year. The first one has been done for you.

1. charlayne hunter-gault was born in south carolina on february 27, 1942.

Charlayne Hunter-Gault was born in South Carolina on February 27, 1942.

2. in 1961, charlayne hunter-gault was a student at the university of georgia.

In 1961 Charlayne Hunter-Gauls Was a student University of Georgia

3. she and hamilton holmes were the first black students at this athens, georgia school.

She and Hamilton holmes were the first Black at this athens, Georgia school.

4. she worked for *the new yorker* and *the new york times*.

She Worked for the New yorke and the New york times

5. charlayne's report on troubles in south africa won the george foster peabody award.

Charlyne's repor on troubles in south africa Won the George foster peabody award.

▶ Here are the eight vocabulary words for this lesson:

confident	difficult	reporter	interfere
university	injustice	informed	riot

▶ There are four blank spaces in the story below. Four vocabulary words have already been used in the story. They are underlined. Use the other four words to fill in the blank spaces.

   One day, Charlayne Hunter-Gault was
_____informed_____ that she was going to a new school.
She would be the first black female student there.
Charlayne knew she would have a difficult time. Some
people did not want her at the _____university_____. They
tried to interfere in many ways. They thought that a
_____riot_____ would frighten the new student. But
Charlayne was confident. She did not let this
_____injustice_____ keep her from her dream. She was
going to learn to be a reporter. Charlayne would not let
this dream slip away.

▶ On a separate sheet of paper or in your notebook, do any one or more of the exercises below for extra credit. Then turn them in to your teacher.

1 It was not easy for Charlayne Hunter-Gault to listen to people yell at her and call her names. Write a paragraph telling how you think Charlayne felt the night a brick came through her window. Explain how you would have felt.

2 Charlayne says, "If people are informed, they will do the right thing." Explain what she means by this. Do you agree with Charlayne? Why or why not?

3 Most people have a favorite reporter. This reporter may give the news on television. He or she may write for a newspaper or magazine. Who is your favorite reporter? Explain what is special about this person.

2

RIDE 'EM COWHAND

The rider settled his boots into the stirrups. He grabbed the rope with his left hand. "Let 'em rip!" he yelled. The gray horse exploded out of the chute. It leaped high into the air. It landed stiff-legged. The rider was jarred . He held on tightly to the reins. His feet came loose from the stirrups. The horse twisted, spun, and reared . It couldn't shake the rider out of the saddle . Ten seconds passed. The cowhand had stayed on past the time limit.

This event is part of a rodeo . A rodeo is a show in which cowhands perform acts of horsemanship and roping. *Rodeo* means roundup in Spanish. In the old days, the ranch hands held contests to test their skills. Wild horses had to be broken for ranch work. Cowhands had to use horses and ropes to help brand the cattle. These tests of skills became part of the modern rodeo.

A rodeo is made up of five main events. One is saddle riding, or bronco busting. The other four are bareback riding, steer wrestling, calf roping, and bull riding.

The riding and roping events are dangerous. Torn muscles, chipped teeth, and broken bones are common. Yet, in spite of these dangers, rodeo performers seldom quit. They only give up when injury or old age makes it impossible to continue.

~~~~~~ MAKE A LIST ~~~~~~

▶ **There are eight vocabulary words in this lesson. In the story, they are boxed in color. Copy the vocabulary words here.**

1. _Jarred_   5. _perform_

2. _reared_   6. _Brand_

3. _Saddle_   7. _Modern_

4. _Rodeo_   8. _injury_

▶ Here are the eight words you copied on the previous page. Write them in alphabetical order in the blank spaces below.

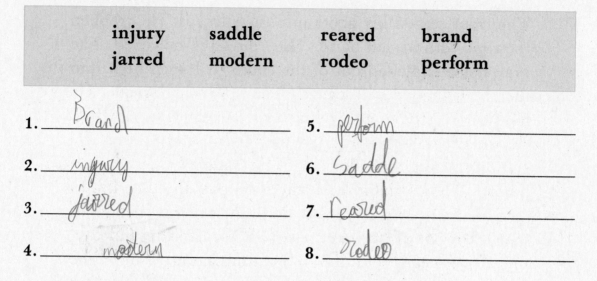

| injury | saddle | reared | brand |
| jarred | modern | rodeo | perform |

1. _Brand_   5. _perform_

2. _injury_   6. _Saddle_

3. _jarred_   7. _reared_

4. _modern_   8. _rodeo_

▶ Here are some meanings for the eight vocabulary words in this lesson. Four words have been written beside their meanings. Write the other four words next to their meanings.

1. _____saddle_____ leather seat for a rider on horseback

2. _____ new; up-to-date

3. _____perform_____ do; act

4. _____ a public show for the skills of cowboys and cowgirls

5. _____jarred_____ shaken; jolted

6. _____ stood on hind legs; done by a horse

7. _____ a wound or damage

8. _____brand_____ to make a mark on the skin with a hot iron

12

▶ Look at the picture. What words come into your mind?
Write them on the blank lines below. To help you get
started, here are two good words:

1. _____ride_____   5. _____

2. _____strong_____   6. _____

3. _____   7. _____

4. _____   8. _____

▶ A **synonym** is a word that means the same, or nearly the same, as another word. *Happy* and *glad* are synonyms.

▶ The column on the left contains the eight key words in the story. To the right of each key word are three other words or groups of words. Two of these are synonyms for the key word. Circle the two synonyms.

1. **jarred**	shaken	jolted	rode
2. **rodeo**	circus	show	roundup
3. **brand**	make a mark	make fun	make a sign
4. **saddle**	seat	place for rider	seat at rodeo
5. **perform**	to act	to do	to lie
6. **injury**	quit	harm	damage
7. **modern**	old	new	up-to-date
8. **reared**	stood on hind legs	afraid to move	front legs off the ground

▶ In each of the following sentences there are words which need capital letters. Rewrite each sentence so the words are correctly capitalized. Remember that capital letters are used in the following places: first word in a sentence; names of people, events, cities, states, countries, and other places; days of the week; months of the year. The first one has been done for you.

1. casey tibbs and jim shoulders have both appeared at frontier days.

Casey Tibbs and Jim Shoulders have both appeared at Frontier Days.

2. we have two tickets for the rodeo at madison square garden on april 4.

3. angela is the best calf roper at the rocky ranch.

4. among the movie stars to appear at the pendleton roundup are robert redford and burt reynolds.

5. the bucking horse in the corral belongs to marge and jenny clarke from winding hills, south dakota.

▶ **Here are the eight vocabulary words for this lesson:**

brand	rodeo	saddle	injury
modern	perform	jarred	reared

▶ **There are four blank spaces in the story below. Four vocabulary words have already been used in the story. They are underlined. Use the other four words to fill in the blank spaces.**

For many people, the days of the cowhands ended years ago. The ranges got smaller. There were fewer cattle to <u>brand</u> with hot irons. The _____ cowhand seemed to be spending more time in a pickup truck than on a bucking bronco. But for a few weeks a year, the Old West returned. That's when the <u>rodeo</u> came to town.

The cowhands and Native Americans paraded through town. The chief sat proudly in his <u>saddle</u>. The crowd cheered as the riders got ready to _____ . Then the contests were on. A wild mustang twisted and _____ . The crowd roared. The rider received an <u>injury</u>, but he held on. No matter how much his horse _____ him, the rider wanted to stay on for at least ten seconds. He made it. For a moment, the good old days of the Wild West had returned.

▶ On a separate sheet of paper or in your notebook, do any one or more of the exercises below for extra credit. Then turn them in to your teacher.

1 Have you ever seen a rodeo? If you have, describe what you think is the most exciting event of the rodeo. Since many of your classmates may not know too much about rodeos, give as many details as possible. If you can, list all the events in a modern rodeo.

2 One of the exercises mentions Casey Tibbs and Jim Shoulders. These are two famous riders who have won the All-Around Cowboy Award many times. Can you give us the names of other riders and the contests they have won? Articles in your local newspapers or national magazines may help you.

3 For many of us, the days of the Old West are gone. Do you believe that is good or bad? List three things that you like about the old days of the cowboy. List three things that were bad about the Old West. You will have to use your imagination for this exercise.

3

HIS CAREER PUMPS IRON

Arnold Schwarzenegger was a teenager in Austria who wanted to try out for a local soccer team. So he lifted weights. Soon he forgot about soccer and became dedicated to weight-lifting. He entered several body-building contests and won them all, including the Mr. Universe title five times and Mr. Olympia seven times. "I was driven and ambitious," he says. "There was no place to go but America."

He worked hard to develop his body. Luckily for Arnold, a book, and later a movie, called *Pumping Iron,* made him famous. His wit , dedication, and ambition won him many fans.

Each time Arnold had money, he invested it carefully. "You don't only have to make the money," he points out, "you have to know how to spend it wisely." His fortune today is estimated to be about thirty million dollars.

Arnold has a new ambition. He wants to be taken seriously as an actor. Reviewers are critical , but Arnold has come too far to stop now. From a young Austrian athlete to a major motion picture star, Arnold Schwarzenegger has demonstrated that you are what you believe you can be.

~~~~~~~~~~~~~~~~~~~~~ MAKE A LIST ~~~~~~~~~~~~~~~~~~~~~

▶ **There are eight vocabulary words in this lesson. In the story, they are boxed in color. Copy the vocabulary words here.**

1. _____   5. _____

2. _____   6. _____

3. _____   7. _____

4. _____   8. _____

▶ Here are the eight words you copied on the previous page. Write them in alphabetical order in the blank spaces below.

local	driven	wit	invested
estimated	reviewers	critical	demonstrated

1._____   5._____

2._____   6._____

3._____   7._____

4._____   8._____

▶ Here are some meanings for the eight vocabulary words in this lesson. Four words have been written beside their meanings. Write the other four words next to their meanings.

1._____reviewers_____people who tell about new films

2._____ambitious; filled with the need to succeed

3._____wit_____humor; intelligence

4._____guessed at the size or value of something

5._____local_____of a small area; regional

6._____disapproving; not supportive

7._____invested_____put money into

8._____showed; proved

20

▶ Look at the picture. What words come into your mind? Write them on the blank lines below. To help you get started, here are two good words:

1. _____powerful_____   5. _____

2. _____famous_____   6. _____

3. _____   7. _____

4. _____   8. _____

▶ A **synonym** is a word that means the same, or nearly the same, as another word. *Happy* and *glad* are synonyms.

▶ The column on the left contains the eight key words in the story. To the right of each key word are three other words or groups of words. Two of these are synonyms for the key word. Circle the two synonyms.

1. **wit**	foolish	humor	intelligence
2. **driven**	determined	failed	having a goal
3. **invested**	put money in	bought into something	took money out
4. **demonstrated**	showed	given proof	sold
5. **local**	national	regional	of a small area
6. **reviewers**	critics	fans	judges
7. **estimated**	owed	guessed	predicted
8. **critical**	unkind	not approving	not judging

▶ The **subject** of a sentence tells what is being talked or written about. It can be one word or a group of words. The underlined words in these sentences are subjects.

Arnold lifted weights as a teenager.
He became very interested in bodybuilding.

▶ **Underline the subjects in the following sentences. The first one has been done for you.**

1. An actor has to be more than handsome.

2. Many skills make a good actor.

3. Movies require timing and talent.

4. Many younger producers want Schwarzenegger for their films.

5. Serious acting is not usually seen as one of his abilities.

6. Mr. Universe is a difficult title to win.

7. His young wife is a niece of President Kennedy.

8. He and his wife live in California.

▶ Here are the eight vocabulary words for this lesson:

local	driven	wit	invested
estimated	reviewers	critical	demonstrated

▶ Four vocabulary words have already been used in the story below. They are underlined. There are four blank spaces in the story. Use the other four vocabulary words to fill in the blank spaces.

It is not always easy to become a famous star. You may have been very successful in _____ events, but that doesn't mean you will have fans all over the country. Also, reviewers can be harmful. If their remarks are _____ , your career can come to a full stop. Many actors have not estimated the amount of damage a bad review can do.

If you are still _____ to become famous, here are some tips. You must have demonstrated some talent that people will admire. You should have a quick and unforgettable _____ . People like to repeat what you have said. Finally, in case your career doesn't work out, it pays to have invested your earnings wisely!

▶ **On a separate sheet of paper or in your notebook, do any one or more of the exercises below for extra credit. Then turn them in to your teacher.**

1 Suppose that you wanted to be a world champion body builder. Write a description of your daily routine. What exercises and foods would you need to reach your goal?

2 Arnold Schwarzenegger is known as a body builder and a star. How might this prevent his becoming a serious actor? Write a list of reasons. Be sure to explain your reasons.

3 Arnold Schwarzenegger is not the only body builder to become famous. Many other famous people use weightlifting to get in shape or to stay in shape. How many famous people can you name who have used weight-lifting in their careers?

4

THE PEOPLE'S CHOICE

It was Tuesday night, November 7, 1989. Like millions of others, David Dinkins watched the election results on TV. The votes were in. He was the winner. He gave a thumbs-up sign. David Norman Dinkins was the first black **mayor** of New York City, the largest city in the **nation** .

David Dinkins is a quiet, good-hearted man. During the **race** for mayor, his friends were afraid he would appear to be **dull** . They were worried that people would not vote for him. But, in his own quiet way, Dinkins is tough. He promised to **combat** crime. He said he would put "a cop in every subway train." He also planned to add something to Gracie Mansion. He wanted his new home to have a swing set on the front lawn.

Although David Dinkins is quiet, he excited the black people of New York. Whenever he visited a black neighborhood, he was given a hero's welcome. People would **applaud** and shout. They would run up to his car. Then they would ask for his **autograph** .

But Dinkins did not just speak for African Americans in New York. He wanted everyone to know that he cared. Voters believed him when he **pledged** to be the "mayor of all of the people."

~~~~~~~~~~~~~~~~~~~~~~ MAKE A LIST ~~~~~~~~~~~~~~~~~~~~~~

▶ **There are eight vocabulary words in this lesson. In the story, they are boxed in color. Copy the vocabulary words here.**

1. _____   5. _____

2. _____   6. _____

3. _____   7. _____

4. _____   8. _____

> Here are the eight words you copied on the previous page. Write then in alphabetical order in the blank spaces below.

combat	autograph	mayor	dull
pledged	race	applaud	nation

1. _____   5. _____

2. _____   6. _____

3. _____   7. _____

4. _____   8. _____

~~~~~~~~ WHAT DO THE WORDS MEAN? ~~~~~~~~

> Here are some meanings for the eight vocabulary words in this lesson. Four words have been written beside their meanings. Write the other four words next to their meanings.

1. _____ a country

2. _____race_____ a contest, often for a job in government

3. _____combat_____ to fight or work against; to try to remove

4. _____ hand-written name; signature, especially of a famous person

5. _____mayor_____ the head of a city

6. _____ not interesting; boring

7. _____pledged_____ made a strong promise

8. _____ to clap one's hands together (to show enjoyment or respect)

▶ Look at the picture. What words come into your mind? Write them on the blank lines below. To help you get started, here are two good words:

1. _____winner_____   5. _____

2. _____mustache_____   6. _____

3. _____   7. _____

4. _____   8. _____

〰〰〰〰〰〰〰   〰〰〰〰〰〰〰

▶ A **synonym** is a word that means the same, or nearly the same, as another word. *Happy* and *glad* are synonyms.

▶ The column on the left contains the eight key words in the story. To the right of each key word are three other words or groups of words. Two of these are synonyms for the key word. Circle the two synonyms.

1. race	job	contest	competition
2. dull	uninteresting	boring	understanding
3. pledged	promised	refused	vowed
4. autograph	name	signature	photograph
5. combat	annoy	fight	battle
6. nation	country	avenue	land
7. applaud	clap	dismiss	cheer
8. mayor	leader	head of a city	senator

▶ Many words end in *ed, er* or *ing*. These endings can change the meaning of a word or form a new word. **Add the right ending to the word before each sentence. Then write the new word in the blank space. Remember, sometimes you drop the final *e* before adding the ending. The first one has been done for you.**

1. **watch**   David Dinkins was ___watching___ the election results on television.

2. **excite**   Dinkins' friends were afraid that his speeches would not be _____ .

3. **speak**   He turned out to be a better _____ than people thought.

4. **combat**   Dinkins plans to use more police for _____ crime.

5. **pledge**   He _____ to work for all the people of New York City.

6. **visit**   Dinkins spent time _____ many neighborhoods.

7. **applaud**   The crowd _____ wildly.

8. **believe**   People _____ in what David Dinkins said.

▶ **Here are the eight vocabulary words for this lesson:**

race	nation	dull	autograph
mayor	combat	applaud	pledged

▶ **There are four blank spaces in the story below. Four vocabulary words have already been used in the story. They are underlined. Use the other four words to fill in the blank spaces.**

David Dinkins had been Manhattan Borough President. He had also served in the New York Assembly. Then, on November 7, 1989, he won his greatest_____. He proudly accepted the second toughest job in the _____.

Running a big city like New York is never _____. David Dinkins has to <u>combat</u> many different kinds of problems. He has <u>pledged</u> to make his city a better place in which to live.

David Dinkins is a quiet man. But people <u>applaud</u> when he speaks. They would like to have his <u>autograph</u>. David Dinkins made history when he became New York City's first black_____.

▶ **On a separate sheet of paper or in your notebook, do any one or more of the exercises below for extra credit. Then turn them in to your teacher.**

1 Before being elected mayor, David Dinkins was Manhattan Borough President. He had also served in the New York Assembly. Find out more about the life of David Dinkins. Ask your librarian to help you.

2 Being mayor of New York City has been called the second toughest job in the country. What are some of the problems the mayor of a large city has to face? What would you do if you were elected mayor of your city or town?

3 To be successful, a mayor needs many skills. Make a list of the special qualities or skills a mayor would need. Then explain how a mayor might use one of the skills you listed. Here are a few to get you started: intelligence, experience, energy.

A DIFFERENT DRUMMER

It is unusual enough that a twenty-three year old woman is the drummer with the otherwise all-male band of the *Arsenio Hall* television show. It seemed even more unusual that she began drumming at the age of seven.

On the other hand, perhaps it isn't so strange. Terri Lyne Carrington has a family **connection** to **quality** jazz. Her grandfather, Matt Carrington, played with jazz greats Fats Waller and Chuck Berry. Terri Lyne was **literally** raised on jazz. At the age of six, she began her professional career with Rahsaan Roland Kirk, a blind musician. She was only ten when she played with pianist Oscar Peterson and trumpeter Dizzy Gillespie. Exciting as the life was, Carrington admits, "I didn't know I was doing anything **extraordinary** . To me they were all just normal people."

She got her television band job by being extraordinary herself. The band's director says, "She had what all the others had plus her own **essence** . She can pull out at any moment some **staggering** **display** ." Carrington is more modest. "I was able to grow and develop each night," she says. Carrington faces an exciting future traveling to the **beat** of her own different drum.

MAKE A LIST

▶ **There are eight vocabulary words in this lesson. In the story, they are boxed in color. Copy the vocabulary words here.**

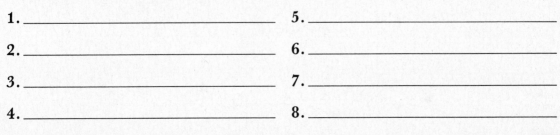

1._____   5._____

2._____   6._____

3._____   7._____

4._____   8._____

▶ Here are the eight words you copied on the previous page. Write them in alphabetical order in the blank spaces below.

connection	quality	literally	extraordinary
essence	staggering	display	beat

1. _____

2. _____

3. _____

4. _____

5. _____

6. _____

7. _____

8. _____

~~~~~~~~~ WHAT DO THE WORDS MEAN? ~~~~~~~~~

▶ Here are some meanings for the eight vocabulary words in this lesson. Four words have been written beside their meanings. Write the other four words next to their meanings.

1. _____staggering_____ overwhelming

2. _____ demonstration

3. _____literally_____ actually

4. _____ of obvious excellence

5. _____essence_____ basic character

6. _____ very unusual

7. _____beat_____ rhythm of a piece of music

8. _____ link

▶ Look at the picture. What words come into your mind?
Write them on the blank lines below. To help you get
started, here are two good words:

1. _____talented_____   5. _____

2. _____exciting_____   6. _____

3. _____   7. _____

4. _____   8. _____

▶ A **synonym** is a word that means the same, or nearly the same, as another word. *Happy* and *glad* are synonyms.

▶ **The column on the left contains the eight key words in the story. To the right of each key word are three other words or groups of words. Two of these are synonyms for the key word. Circle the two synonyms.**

1. **extraordinary**	impossible	remarkable	unusual
2. **display**	performance	opening	show
3. **quality**	excellent	fine	fair
4. **staggering**	terrible	unexpected	amazing
5. **essence**	core	very good	base
6. **literally**	written	truly	exactly
7. **beat**	musical pulse	mix	rhythm
8. **connection**	attachment	link	plug

▶ **Verbs** are words which express action or being. The underlined words in these sentences are verbs.

<u>Go</u> to the concert.
Terry <u>is</u> a great drummer.
<u>Can</u> she <u>play</u> any other instrument?

▶ **Underline the verbs in the following sentences. The first one has been done for you.**

1. Terri Lyne Carrington <u>played</u> at the age of five.

2. She has performed with many jazz greats.

3. Have you seen her work on the *Arsenio Hall* show?

4. She drums brilliantly and she enjoys the show.

5. Who is the leader of that band?

6. Well, everyone likes the music.

7. Carrington always has a special quality.

8. She almost did not try the drums.

▶ **Here are the eight vocabulary words for this lesson:**

connection	quality	literally	extraordinary
essence	staggering	display	beat

▶ **There are four blank spaces in the story below. Four vocabulary words have already been used in the story. They are underlined. Use the other four words to fill in the blank spaces.**

Terri Lyne Carrington has many _____ to jazz. Her grandfather played with some famous musicians. She also showed an _____ talent when she was only five years old. Her talent was on _____ in concerts before she was ten. Her skill was staggering to many people who expected undeveloped talent.

Jazz has literally given her life its direction. She even won a scholarship at the age of eleven. She plays quality music in every band she joins. Her drums set the _____ for the other players, yet all her performances somehow capture the essence of this remarkable young woman. Hers is a career to watch.

▶ **On a separate sheet of paper or in your notebook, do any one or more of the exercises below for extra credit. Then turn them in to your teacher.**

1 Would you like to play a musical instrument? Which would you play? Why do you think you would like it? Write reasons for each of your opinions.

2 Do you think Terri Lyne Carrington should have been allowed to play in concerts when she was less than ten years old? Why do you or don't you think so? Give reasons to support your opinion.

3 Music has a language of its own. When writers refer to time, they don't mean the hour. Test your musical knowledge. What do these words or expressions mean— note, chord, bar, measure, beat, hot, jazz, jam, blues, gig, group?

⊹ 6 MOUNTAIN OF ICE ⊹

The *Titanic* was supposed to be one of the safest ships in the world. On April 14, 1912, the *Titanic* was crossing the Atlantic Ocean. The night was foggy but the passengers were not worried. Suddenly, there was a **horrible** noise. The *Titanic* had hit an **iceberg** ! At 2:05 A.M. the *Titanic* sank. More than 1,500 people drowned.

An iceberg is an **immense** piece of ice which floats in the ocean. *Berg* is the German word for mountain. So iceberg means mountain of ice. Icebergs are dangerous because they are so big. But only a very small part of an iceberg is **visible** . The rest of the iceberg is **beneath** the surface of the water.

Icebergs are really the snows of hundreds or thousands of years ago. Icebergs start as snowfall in Greenland. Because it is so cold, very little snow melts. As more snow falls, the snow gets thick and hard. The bottom turns to ice. This ice, moving slowly toward the sea, is called a **glacier** . When a **chunk** of the glacier falls into the sea, it is called an iceberg. An iceberg is moved south by wind and ocean currents. If it floats far enough south, a ship may run into the iceberg. This happened to the *Titanic*.

The International Ice Patrol was **established** soon after the sinking of the *Titanic*. Since that time, no ships have been lost because of icebergs.

⌇⌇⌇⌇⌇⌇⌇⌇⌇⌇⌇ MAKE A LIST ⌇⌇⌇⌇⌇⌇⌇⌇⌇⌇⌇

▶ **There are eight vocabulary words in this lesson. In the story, they are boxed in color. Copy the vocabulary words here.**

1. _____   5. _____

2. _____   6. _____

3. _____   7. _____

4. _____   8. _____

▶ Here are the eight words you copied on the previous page. Write them in alphabetical order in the blank spaces below.

| immense | chunk | glacier | visible |
| beneath | horrible | established | iceberg |

1. _____   5. _____

2. _____   6. _____

3. _____   7. _____

4. _____   8. _____

~~~~~~~~ WHAT DO THE WORDS MEAN? ~~~~~~~~

▶ Here are some meanings for the eight vocabulary words in this lesson. Four words have been written beside their meanings. Write the other four words next to their meanings.

1. _____chunk_____ a short, thick piece; good-sized portion

2. _____ can be seen; can be observed

3. _____iceberg_____ mountain of ice; large chunk of ice broken off from a glacier

4. _____ below; underneath

5. _____horrible_____ terrible; frightful

6. _____ set up; founded

7. _____ huge; very large

8. _____glacier_____ extremely large mass of ice and snow

▶ Look at the picture. What words come into your mind? Write them on the blank lines below. To help you get started, here are two good words:

1. _____porthole_____   5. _____

2. _____crowd_____   6. _____

3. _____   7. _____

4. _____   8. _____

A **synonym** is a word that means the same, or nearly the same, as another word. *Happy* and *glad* are synonyms.

The column on the left contains the eight key words in the story. To the right of each key word are three other words or groups of words. Two of these are synonyms for the key word. Circle the two synonyms.

1. **immense**	moving	very large	huge
2. **chunk**	piece	part	fat
3. **glacier**	mass of ice	moving mountain	huge amount of moving snow
4. **visible**	can be moved	can be seen	can be spotted
5. **established**	destroyed	set up	organized
6. **iceberg**	mountain of ice	melted ice	huge chunk of ice
7. **horrible**	terrible	noisy	very bad
8. **beneath**	below	underneath	besides

▶ A **contraction** is a short form of a word or a word group. For example, *can't* is a contraction of *cannot*. *I'll* is a contraction of *I will*. Contractions are formed by putting an **apostrophe** (') in place of the missing letter or letters. **Write the contractions for the underlined words. The first one has been done for you.**

1. We asked Bob to come with us, but he <u>had not</u> finished his homework.   hadn't

2. <u>We are</u> planning to move to Chicago next month.   _____

3. <u>I am</u> not looking forward to going.   _____

4. <u>She will</u> talk about glaciers every chance she gets.   _____

5. Marsha said that <u>you have</u> actually seen an iceberg.   _____

6. Did you ask <u>who is</u> coming to the party?   _____

47

▶ Here are the eight vocabulary words for this lesson:

glacier	beneath	chunk	iceberg
visible	established	immense	horrible

▶ There are four blank spaces in the story below. Four vocabulary words have already been used in the story. They are underlined. Use the other four words to fill in the blank spaces.

Our ship is moving slowly through icy waters. We have been warned about an iceberg. We know that icebergs are dangerous. Only a small part of the mountain of ice is_____. The rest is hidden beneath the surface of the sea. We are on the lookout for an immense_____ of ice. We do not want to repeat the lesson of the *Titanic*. That _____ accident will never leave our minds. Over 1,500 people died because a great ship hit an iceberg. Many new safety rules had to be _____ because of the *Titanic*.

Since April of 1912, no ship has sunk because of an iceberg. The U. S. Coast Guard and the International Ice Patrol watch carefully. They know that icebergs break off from a glacier. They watch these slow-moving masses of ice and warn all nearby ships.

▶ **On a separate sheet of paper or in your notebook, do any one or more of the exercises below for extra credit. Then turn them in to your teacher.**

1 The sinking of the *Titanic* was the worst disaster in the history of the sea. Many books and news stories have been written about it. See how much information you can add to the story. For example, do you know that the *Titanic* was thought to be unsinkable?

2 The story says that "an iceberg is moved south by wind and ocean currents." Do you know that scientists are working on plans to tow icebergs to warmer climates? They would use the icebergs to supply water for dry lands. Does this make sense to you? Explain.

3 Look at the vocabulary words *iceberg* and *glacier*. Together they are made up of 14 letters. See how many words you can form by using the letters of these words. Make up at least ten words. Here are some words to get you started: clear, rice, bigger.

SEARCHING FOR ROOTS

Alex Haley had a strong desire . He wanted to know where his family came from. He searched records for 12 years. He **traced** his family back to Africa. He met a storyteller in Gambia on the west coast of Africa. The storyteller told Haley about his great-great-grandfather Kunta Kinte. Haley learned how Kunta was caught by slavers. He was chained and thrown into the hold of a slave ship. Life on board was horrible.

Haley studied the history of Kunta and his descendants in America. He wrote their story in his book *Roots*. It became a best seller. Haley became famous. Later, a short TV **series** based on the book ran for eight nights. It **attracted** an audience of millions. Americans saw how slaves were treated. They had no rights. They were cruelly **separated** from their families. Their masters treated them harshly. The book and the series showed how Kunta and his **descendants** fought to become free.

Haley feels that all of us are searching for our roots. He believes that we should get to know our families and their histories better. Then we will **discover** things about our past we might never have known. Haley never gave up searching for his roots. His **ancestor** Kunta never gave up his search for freedom.

MAKE A LIST

▶ **There are eight vocabulary words in this lesson. In the story, they are boxed in color. Copy the vocabulary words here.**

1. _____   5. _____

2. _____   6. _____

3. _____   7. _____

4. _____   8. _____

▶ Here are the eight words you copied on the previous page. Write them in alphabetical order in the blank spaces below.

| series | discover | attracted | desire |
| ancestor | separated | traced | descendants |

1._____   5._____

2._____   6._____

3._____   7._____

4._____   8._____

▶ Here are some meanings for the eight vocabulary words in this lesson. Four words have been written beside their meanings. Write the other four words next to their meanings.

1._____series_____ TV show that appears each week

2._____ apart; not together

3._____traced_____ followed; tracked

4._____ find out; uncover

5.____descendants____ people born of a certain family; heirs

6._____ gathered; brought together

7._____desire_____ wish; purpose

8._____ great-grandparent or one who came before

▶ Look at the picture. What words come into your mind? Write them on the blank lines below. To help you get started, here are two good words:

1. _____hat_____   5. _____

2. _____characters____   6. _____

3. _____   7. _____

4. _____   8. _____

▶ A **synonym** is a word that means the same, or nearly the same, as another word. *Happy* and *glad* are synonyms.

▶ The column on the left contains the eight key words in the story. To the right of each key word are three other words or groups of words. Two of these are synonyms for the key word. Circle the two synonyms.

1. **attracted**	brought together	separated	gathered
2. **traced**	located	tracked down	wrote about
3. **descendants**	heirs	fighters	children
4. **desire**	wish	intention	hatred
5. **separated**	apart	attracted	not together
6. **series**	in a row	breakfast food	weekly TV show
7. **ancestor**	great-grandmother	aunt and uncle	great-grandfather
8. **discover**	uncover	find out	leave

▶ These five sentences have been scrambled or mixed up. Write the words in the correct order so that they make complete sentences. The first one has been done for you.

1. book called Alex *Roots* a Haley wrote

   Alex Haley wrote a book called *Roots*.
   _____

2. is country in Gambia a Africa
   _____

3. America people to from countries many other come
   _____

4. grandparents to Italy moved my Chicago from
   _____

5. Cicely *Roots* of stars one Tyson was the of
   _____

▶ Here are the eight vocabulary words for this lesson:

series	ancestor	discover	separated
attracted	traced	desire	descendants

▶ There are four blank spaces in the story below. Four vocabulary words have already been used in the story. They are underlined. Use the other four words to fill in the blank spaces.

Almost anyone can <u>discover</u> his or her roots. Alex Haley _____ his roots back to Africa. His _____ Kunta Kinte had come from Africa. He was <u>separated</u> from his family and sold as a slave. Kunta Kinte's _____ found about their past through Haley's research. They and millions of other people read Haley's book or watched the TV <u>series</u>. Many North Americans are _____ to the idea of finding out where they came from. It is a strong <u>desire</u> that many of us share.

▶ **On a separate sheet of paper or in your notebook, do any one or more of the exercises below for extra credit. Then turn them in to your teacher.**

1 Did you ever think about your last name, or your first name, and how you got it? Talk to as many members of your family as you can. Ask them if they know what country your ancestors came from. Ask them if your name means anything special.

2 Why was it hard for Alex Haley to find out about his ancestors? Would it be more or less difficult for someone whose ancestors had not been slaves? Why? Explain your answer in two or three sentences.

3 See if you can find out more about your ancestors. Talk to members of your family. See if you can find pictures or photographs of your ancestors. Use this information to write a short history of your family.

Would you like to know your future? Many would jump at the opportunity to find out what will happen to them. Some people go to astrologers. These people study the planets to tell the future.

Astrologers need to know the exact time and place of your birth. They then make up a chart of the heavens. It shows where the sun and moon were then. It also shows where the other planets were.

Astrologers divide the heavens into 12 equal parts. Each part is named after a group of stars. The starting group is Aries, the Ram. Taurus, the Bull, follows. Ten other groups, or signs, follow. The names of the signs came from an ancient people.

Astrologers believe that people behave the way they do because of their signs. For example, those born under the sign of Aries are ambitious . They want to get ahead. Those born under the sign of Leo are said to be generous . They are willing to share.

Scientists believe that astrology is nonsense. They think it is based on superstition . They say that we act the way we do because of our parents. The way we are raised is important. Scientists do not believe that the position of the stars or planets at the time of birth decides our future . What do you think?

~~~~~~~~~~~~~~ MAKE A LIST ~~~~~~~~~~~~~~

▶ **There are eight vocabulary words in this lesson. In the story, they are boxed in color. Copy the vocabulary words here.**

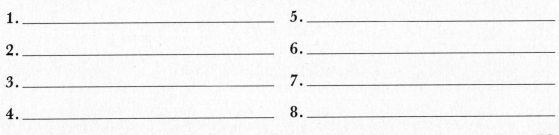

1._____   5._____

2._____   6._____

3._____   7._____

4._____   8._____

▶ Here are the eight words you copied on the previous page. Write them in alphabetical order in the blank spaces below.

opportunity	planets	generous	ancient
chart	superstition	future	ambitious

1. _____   5. _____

2. _____   6. _____

3. _____   7. _____

4. _____   8. _____

▶ Here are some meanings for the eight vocabulary words in this lesson. Four words have been written beside their meanings. Write the other four words next to their meanings.

1. _____future_____ a time to come; what is ahead

2. _____ willing to share

3. _____opportunity_____ a chance, usually a good one

4. _____ any of the nine heavenly bodies that orbit the sun

5. _____superstition_____ belief based on ignorance and fear

6. _____ wanting fame or success

7. _____chart_____ diagram; map or graph

8. _____ belonging to times long past; very old

60

▶ Look at the picture. What words come into your mind?
Write them on the blank lines below. To help you get
started, here are two good words:

1. _____ globe _____   5. _____

2. ___ old-fashioned ___   6. _____

3. _____   7. _____

4. _____   8. _____

▶ A **synonym** is a word that means the same, or nearly the same, as another word. *Happy* and *glad* are synonyms.

▶ The column on the left contains the eight key words in the story. To the right of each key word are three other words or groups of words. Two of these are synonyms for the key word. Circle the two synonyms.

1. **chart**	ship	map	diagram
2. **future**	what is ahead	what is past	the unknown
3. **opportunity**	strange	chance	possibility
4. **superstition**	ignorance	science	fear
5. **generous**	unselfish	rich	caring
6. **ancient**	old	past	mysterious
7. **planets**	heavenly bodies	sun orbiters	Sun
8. **ambitious**	seeking quiet	seeking fame	wanting success

▶ Some words are often confused because they look alike or sound alike. For example, *there* and *their* and *where* and *wear* are often confused. **Place the correct word in the blank spaces in the following sentences. The first one has been done for you.**

1. **(red, read)**   I think I'll have my palm _____read_____ by a fortuneteller.

2. **(pair, pear)**   The fruit Cynthia likes best is a _____.

3. **(cents, sense)**   I have more _____ than to believe in astrology.

4. **(stare, stair)**   Clara was so surprised, all she could do was _____ .

5. **(stake, steak)**   When you put up the tent, make sure each _____ is firmly in the ground.

6. **(bare, bear)**   When we go to the zoo, Katie likes to visit her favorite _____ .

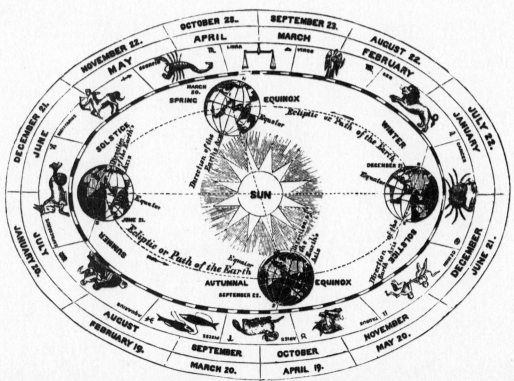

The Constellations, Seasons, Equinoxes, &c.

63

▶ Here are the eight vocabulary words for this lesson:

chart	ancient	opportunity	superstition
future	planets	generous	ambitious

▶ There are four blank spaces in the story below. Four vocabulary words have already been used in the story. They are underlined. Use the other four words to fill in the blank spaces.

Many people don't believe in astrology. They do not think that one's signs at birth are important. _____ or stars have nothing to do with the kind of person you become. Scientists think that superstition makes people believe in astrology. But some people jump at the_____to have their fortunes told. They feel that being ambitious or _____ is all in one's stars. Many ancient people believed in astrology. They made up a _____ of the heavens. Each part is named after a group of stars. These people believed they could tell the future by reading the stars. Do you believe your sign at birth determines what you are today?

▶ **On a separate sheet of paper or in your notebook, do any one or more of the exercises below for extra credit. Then turn them in to your teacher.**

1 Many ancient people believed that the future could be told by reading the stars. Look up astrology in an encyclopedia. Find out about the history of astrology. When did astrology lose its importance? Why?

2 Most newspapers have columns on astrology. Check your own sign and see what the charts tell about you. Ask some of your friends to do the same thing. Check to see how accurate these reports are. Do they make sense?

3 The astrology signs are really groups of stars or constellations. Ask your librarian to help you find diagrams or pictures of some of the stars. Connect the stars with an imaginary line to form the shape the group was named after.

Of course, you know the story of Peter Rabbit. But did you know about the **author** of the story, Beatrix Potter? Potter wrote more than 25 other books and gave us many happy memories from our childhoods.

Potter's own childhood, however, was not so happy. She was raised in a wealthy English family at the end of the 1800s. Her parents were busy and rarely saw her. Fortunately Potter had many pets. She spent her lonely hours drawing and re-drawing the animals that she kept in a family "zoo."

Her first book, *The Tale of Peter Rabbit,* was written for a sick child. She printed the book at her own **expense** because book **publishers** told her the book would not sell. Today, Potter's books sell about seven million copies a year. They are also printed in sixteen other languages. Potter is one of the most successful authors of all time.

Potter had strong feelings for animals and nature. She believed in **conservation** of the countryside and its animals and plants. When she died, she **donated** her large sheep farm to the British people. She also left hundreds of careful drawings of mushrooms, leaves, and animals. These drawings are so **realistic** that museums use them today to identify new additions to their collections. Potter's **great** powers of **observation** gave her a love of nature which she handed down to her readers.

MAKE A LIST

▶ **There are eight vocabulary words in this lesson. In the story, they are boxed in color. Copy the vocabulary words here.**

1. *author*   5. *donated*
2. *expense*   6. *realistic*
3. *publishers*   7. *great*
4. *conservation*   8. *observation*

▶ Here are the eight words you copied on the previous page. Write them in alphabetical order in the blank spaces below.

| author | expense | publisher | conservation |
| donated | realistic | great | observation |

1. _____ 5. _____

2. _____ 6. _____

3. _____ 7. _____

4. _____ 8. _____

▶ Here are some meanings for the eight vocabulary words in this lesson. Four words have been written beside their meanings. Write the other four words next to their meanings.

1. _____conservation_____ protection

2. _____ true, correct

3. _____publisher_____ maker of printed books

4. _____observation_____ attention; watching

5. _____ writer

6. _____ gave

7. _____expense_____ cost

8. _____ much above average

▶ Look at the picture. What words come into your mind? Write them on the blank lines below. To help you get started, here are two good words:

1. _____ kind _____   5. _____

2. _____ cheerful _____   6. _____

3. _____   7. _____

4. _____   8. _____

▶ A **synonym** is a word that means the same, or nearly the same, as another word. *Happy* and *glad* are synonyms.

▶ The column on the left contains the eight words in the story. To the right of each key word are three other words or groups of words. Two of these are synonyms for the key word. Circle the two synonyms.

1. **author**   book creator   book buyer   writer

2. **expense**   cost   loss   price

3. **publisher**   owner of   maker of   distributor of
                      books   books   books

4. **conservation**   preservation   protection   ownership

5. **donated**   gave   presented   lost

6. **realistic**   accurate   violent   lifelike

7. **great**   superior   outstanding   fortunate

8. **observation**   watching   arguing   looking

Some words are often confused because they look alike or sound alike. For example, *there* and *their* and *to* and *too* are often confused. **Place the correct word in each of the blank spaces in the following sentences. The first one has been done as an example.**

1. (there, their)   <u>There</u> was no way for the Potters to know <u>their</u> daughter.

2. (our, hour)   Beatrix saw them for one _____ a day, which is not like _____ lives today.

3. (knew, new)   She _____ real happiness whenever she drew a _____ animal or plant.

4. (pair, pear)   Beatrix might make a drawing of a fresh, ripe _____ or draw a _____ of family pets.

5. (maid, made)   The Potters' _____ cleaned her room and _____ the same lunch for Beatrix each day.

6. (you're, your)   Beatrix might think _____ lucky because you see _____ parents so often.

▷ Here are the eight vocabulary words for this lesson:

author	expense	publisher	conservation
donated	realistic	great	observation

▷ There are four blank spaces in the story below. Four vocabulary words have already been used in the story. They are underlined. Use the other four words to fill in the blank spaces.

Beatrix Potter was the _____ of many children's books. She had great talent and she insisted on _____ details in her stories. Once, she complained when another writer had a toad comb its hair. She pointed out that toads don't really have hair.

Although she had to print her first book at her own _____, Potter quickly became a popular author. In 1913, she married the publisher of her books. They lived on her farm, trying to protect the natural beauty of the English countryside. They became supporters of conservation of the land around them.

Beatrix Potter's close _____ of the countryside can be seen in her books. You can find many of the scenes in her books on actual roads around her house. To protect these beautiful places, she donated her land to the British people. There is a musuem, and you can visit it today.

▶ **On a separate sheet of paper or in your notebook, do any one or more of the exercises below for extra credit. Then turn them in to your teacher.**

1 Try to find out more about Beatrix Potter. Look in an encyclopedia or other book to find out where she lived, when she was born, and when she died. Write a brief paragraph telling what you have learned.

2 Imagine that you are a friend of Beatrix Potter. You have just read *The Tale of Peter Rabbit* for the first time. You know that Beatrix is not sure people will like her stories. Write a letter to Beatrix telling her how much you liked her book. Be sure to use the correct form for a letter.

3 Work with a partner to create a radio interview with Beatrix Potter. One of you will be Potter, the other a radio reporter. Beatrix Potter believed in conservation of the land and wild animals. What might she say about the world today? Make up a list of questions and Potter's answers for your interview.

© 1989 Warner Bros., Inc. All rights reserved.

74

10 CHRIS BURKE
HIS LIFE GOES ON

Chris Burke is an unusual television star. He has never taken acting lessons and he wasn't looking for an acting job. He also has Down's syndrome , a birth defect . Burke likes to call it "Up Syndrome."

Burke was born in 1965. In those days, most babies with Down's syndrome were put in institutions that treat this problem. Burke's parents didn't do that with their son. He was brought up to believe strongly in doing things for himself. He had a job as an elevator operator in New York City. He saw another actor with Down's syndrome and wrote a fan letter. That actor's mother was a television writer, and she mentioned Burke to the producers of a new television show.

His television show, *Life Goes On*, concerns the problems that face a family in day-to-day life. Burke plays one of the children, a boy with Down's syndrome. The show has been well-received, but there is always a struggle for television success.

The show's producer says, "We want to show what someone with a disability is capable of." So far, Burke has shown that he is capable of capturing the nation's heart with his sincere and realistic performance.

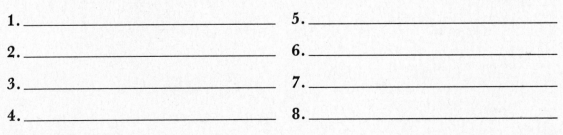

~~~~~~~~~~~~~~~~~~~~~ MAKE A LIST ~~~~~~~~~~~~~~~~~~~~~

▶ **There are eight vocabulary words in this lesson. In this story, they are boxed in color. Copy the vocabulary words here.**

1._____   5._____

2._____   6._____

3._____   7._____

4._____   8._____

▶ Here are the eight words you copied on the previous page. Write them in alphabetical order in the blank spaces below.

syndrome	defect	institutions	operator
mentioned	struggle	capable	capturing

1. _____   5. _____

2. _____   6. _____

3. _____   7. _____

4. _____   8. _____

▶ Here are some meanings for the eight vocabulary words in this lesson. Four words have been written beside their meanings. Write the other four words next to their meanings.

1. ____syndrome____ group of characteristics, or symptoms, indicating a condition

2. _____ spoke about

3. ____defect____ weakness; disability

4. _____ hard work

5. ____institutions____ building housing an organization

6. _____ a person who runs a machine

7. ____capable____ able to do

8. _____ winning; gaining control of

76

© 1989 Warner Bros., Inc. All rights reserved.

〰〰〰〰〰〰〰 USE YOUR OWN WORDS 〰〰〰〰〰〰〰

▶ Look at the picture. What words come into your mind?
Write them on the blank lines below. To help you get
started, here are two good words:

1._____pleasant_____   5._____

2._____eager_____   6._____

3._____   7._____

4._____   8._____

〰〰〰〰〰〰〰〰〰〰   〰〰〰〰〰〰〰

▶ A **synonym** is a word that means the same, or nearly the same, as another word. *Happy* and *glad* are synonyms.

▶ The column on the left contains the eight key words in the story. To the right of each key word are three other words or groups of words. Two of these are synonyms for the key word. Circle the two synonyms.

1. **struggle**	effort	fail	battle
2. **institutions**	care centers	doctors	hospitals
3. **capable**	careless	able to do	skilled
4. **mentioned**	spoke of	remarked	shouted
5. **defect**	imperfection	broke	flaw
6. **capturing**	killing	winning	earning
7. **syndrome**	condition	cure	disorder
8. **operator**	telephone	machinist	user

▶ **Nouns** are words used to name persons (actor), places (city), things (book), actions (acting), ideas (truth), and qualities (honesty). There are two kinds of nouns, *proper* and *common*. Common nouns are names of any persons, places, or things: actor, city, condition. Proper nouns are the names of particular persons, places, or things: Chris Burke, New York City, Down Syndrome.

▶ **Underline the nouns in each of the sentences below. Place one line under each common noun. Place two lines under each proper noun. The first one has been done for you.**

1. Burke, the actor, learns his lines.

2. Mike Braverman is the producer of the program.

3. Chris thinks actors are caring people.

4. Braverman says Burke is a natural actor.

5. Down's syndrome is a common birth defect.

6. Patti LuPone is Burke's mother on the show.

7. Burke and LuPone seem like members of a real family.

8. Frank Burke, the father of the actor, helps with his lines.

© 1989 Warner Bros., Inc. All rights reserved.

▶ Here are the eight vocabulary words for this lesson:

syndrome	defect	institutions	operator
mentioned	struggle	capable	capturing

▶ Four vocabulary words have already been used in the story below. They are underlined. There are four blank spaces in the story. Use the four other vocabulary words to fill in the blank spaces.

People who have a birth <u>defect</u> want to lead lives that are as normal as possible. This story _____ Down's <u>syndrome</u>, but there are other birth defects as well. People with one of these defects are _____ of living on their own. They do not need to be put into _____ . Such a person can be an <u>operator</u> of a machine, or a messenger, or an assistant on many kinds of jobs. However, their real _____ seems to be to get people to accept them.

Recently, people with disabilities are <u>capturing</u> public attention. The President has signed a bill giving these people the legal rights of other Americans. Perhaps the time will come when their disabilities will not seem so important.

▶ On a separate sheet of paper or in your notebook, do any one or more of the exercises below for extra credit. Then turn them in to your teacher.

1 Do you think Burke can continue to have a career as an actor? What kinds of parts could he play? Write your reasons for believing as you do.

2 Ask your librarian to help you find more information about Chris Burke in magazines. You may also find stories about other actors with special conditions. Describe the information you have found about Burke or the other actors.

3 Watch a television show of your choice. Write a review of the show. Tell what you liked or disliked about the show. You might mention how realistic events or characters seemed to you.

Each year, thousands of people go backpacking. Most people hike close to home. And most of them hike less than ten miles each trip. Hikers say backpacking is fun if you are prepared.

First, the hiker must dress properly . To start, you'll need a comfortable shirt and pants. Boots and two pairs of socks are also needed. Many hikers wear two light sweaters. When you get warm, you can remove a sweater. You can put it back on when you stop hiking. This prevents being chilled. A wool hat and gloves help when it is chilly.

Next, the hiker must have food and water. Some hikers carry "gorp" in their packs. Gorp is a snack of fruits, seeds, nuts, and candy. It gives the hiker pep . Freeze-dried foods are also popular. They come in compact packages which are easy to carry. You just have to add boiling water. Minutes later, you have meat, vegetables, and dessert.

Finally, the smart hiker follows a marked trail. Many hikers also use maps and a compass . And many back-packers hike with a companion rather than hiking alone.

How about you? Would you like to try backpacking?

MAKE A LIST

▶ **There are eight vocabulary words in this lesson. In the story, they are boxed in color. Copy the vocabulary words here.**

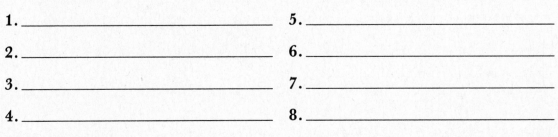

1. _____   5. _____

2. _____   6. _____

3. _____   7. _____

4. _____   8. _____

▶ Here are the eight words you copied on the previous page. Write them in alphabetical order in the blank spaces below.

properly	compact	prevents	remove
pep	hike	companion	compass

1._____ 5._____

2._____ 6._____

3._____ 7._____

4._____ 8._____

▶ Here are some meanings for the eight vocabulary words in this lesson. Four words have been written beside their meanings. Write the other four words next to their meanings.

1._____ take off; take away

2._____ instrument used to tell directions

3._____pep_____ energy; liveliness; spirit

4._____ take a long walk or march

5._____prevents_____ stops; keeps something from happening

6._____ correctly; without mistakes

7.____companion____ friend; pal

8.____compact_____ taking up little space; solidly packed

~~~~~~~~~~~~~~~~~ USE YOUR OWN WORDS ~~~~~~~~~~~~~~~~~

▶ Look at the picture. What words come into your mind?
Write them on the blank lines below. To help you get
started, here are two good words:

1._____ outdoors _____   5._____

2._____ adventure _____   6._____

3._____   7._____

4._____   8._____

▶ A **synonym** is a word that means the same, or nearly the same, as another word. *Happy* and *glad* are synonyms.

▶ The column on the left contains the eight key words in the story. To the right of each key word are three other words or groups of words. Two of these are synonyms for the key word. Circle the two synonyms.

1. **pep**	energy	dullness	liveliness
2. **properly**	correctly	without mistakes	thoughtlessly
3. **companion**	friend	pal	enemy
4. **remove**	take on	take off	take away
5. **hike**	march	ride	walk far
6. **compact**	space-saving	loosely packed	solidly packed
7. **compass**	pointer	helps guide you	holds packages
8. **prevents**	stops	packs	keeps from happening

▶ A **contraction** is a short form of a word or a word group. For example, *can't* is a contraction of *cannot*. *I'll* is a contraction of *I will*. Contractions are formed by putting an apostrophe (') in place of the missing letter or letters. **Write the contractions for the underlined words. The first one has been done for you.**

1. A smart hiker <u>does not</u> hike alone. _____doesn't_____

2. <u>It is</u> important to wear the right clothes when hiking. _____

3. Make sure <u>you are</u> wearing two pairs of socks. _____

4. <u>Do not</u> hike on an unfamiliar trail in the winter. _____

5. After hiking a trail in warm weather, <u>you will</u> be ready to hike it in winter. _____

6. I <u>have not</u> had the opportunity to go backpacking. _____

▶ **Here are the eight vocabulary words for this lesson:**

properly	compact	prevents	remove
pep	hike	companion	compass

▶ **There are four blank spaces in the story below. Four vocabulary words have already been used in the story. They are underlined. Use the other four words to fill in the blank spaces.**

Each year, many people strap on a backpack, take a compass in hand, and _____ through the woods. The smart hiker always lets someone know where he or she will be hiking. Many people like to go backpacking with a _____ or two. People hiking together can watch out for one another. They should make sure they rest often. Smart hikers take "snack breaks," too. Eating can restore a hiker's pep.

Backpackers are busy hiking all year long. But when the weather turns cold, some people stop hiking. Other hikers take care to dress _____. They dress in layers that they can remove easily. This prevents the body from getting too hot too fast. A small, _____ pack can carry almost everything a hiker needs.

But remember, backpacking is not a game. It can be fun if you are careful and well-prepared.

▶ **On a separate sheet of paper or in your notebook, do any one or more of the exercises below for extra credit. Then turn them in to your teacher.**

1 Make a list of at least five things a smart backpacker should carry in a backpack. Write a sentence telling why each thing is important.

2 Look at the vocabulary words *companion* and *hike*. Together they are made up of 13 letters. See how many words you can form by using the letters of these words. Make up at least ten words. Here are some words to get you started: poke, phone, nice.

3 Have you ever gone backpacking or hiking? Describe your experience. Tell where you have gone, how far, and any interesting things you can remember.

Most of us know Bill Cosby as a famous comic and actor. His stories of Fat Albert and Weird Harold make us laugh. He has won awards as an actor. His television program, *The Cosby Show*, was the most popular show of the 80s. But Bill Cosby is also a student. He knows the value of learning. Even though he finished three years at Temple University, he wanted to learn more. So Bill returned to school. Between concerts and TV shows, he studied at the University of Massachusetts. He was a part-time student for seven years. Then, at age 39, Bill finally finished school. He earned the degree of Doctor of Education. This is the highest title given in the field of education . It took years of study and hard work to get this degree.

The path to success was not easy. Bill had been a dropout twice. After the tenth grade, he left school to join the Navy. While in the Navy, he took courses by mail and received his high school diploma. Later, he left college to go into show business. But he always wanted to guide kids. So he combined his ability to make kids laugh and his education. Most of the shows he has been in, like *Sesame Street* and *The Electric Company*, use TV to teach. They are concerned with reading and writing. They mix learning with laughter. So while kids are laughing with Doctor Bill, they are learning, too.

MAKE A LIST

▶ **There are eight vocabulary words in this lesson. In the story, they are boxed in color. Copy the vocabulary words here.**

1. Comic

2. Value

3. earned

4. degree

5. education

6. path

7. guide

8. concerned

▶ Here are the eight words you copied on the previous page. Write them in alphabetical order in the blank spaces below.

comic	degree	education	guide
value	earned	path	concerned

1. _Comic_   5. _education_

2. _concerned_   6. _guide_

3. _degree_   7. _path_

4. _earned_   8. _value_

~~~~~~~~~ WHAT DO THE WORDS MEAN? ~~~~~~~~~

▶ Here are some meanings for the eight vocabulary words in this lesson. Four words have been written beside their meanings. Write the other four words next to their meanings.

1. _____path_____ a road or track

2. _____guide_____ interested in someone or something

3. _____degree_____ a paper or diploma showing someone has graduated, usually from college

4. _____value_____ the worth of something

5. _____earned_____ gained as a result of hard work; acquired

6. _____comic_____ a person who makes you laugh

7. _____education_____ the process of learning; gained knowledge

8. _____path_____ direct; show the way

92

~~~~~~~~~~~~~ USE YOUR OWN WORDS ~~~~~~~~~~~~~

▶ Look at the picture. What words come into your mind?
Write them on the blank lines below. To help you get
started, here are two good words:

1. _____ comedy _____   5. _old_____

2. _____ springs _____   6. _talkg allot_____

3. _____ Smart _____   7. _family_____

4. _____ fitch _____   8. _interesting_____

~~~~~~

▶ A **synonym** is a word that means the same, or nearly the same, as another word. *Happy* and *glad* are synonyms.

▶ The column on the left contains the eight key words in the story. To the right of each key word are three other words or groups of words. Two of these are synonyms for the key word. Circle the two synonyms.

1. **degree**   study   (diploma)   award

2. **comic**   (comedian)   student   funny person

3. **guide**   follow   (lead)   direct

4. **path**   (road)   footprint   track

5. **education**   learning   building   (knowledge)

6. **concerned**   (interested)   foolish   involved

7. **value**   jewelry   (worth)   price

8. **earned**   (gained)   acquired   lost

▶ Two of the words used in the story, *path* and *actor,* are **nouns**. Think of your favorite actor and a path you know well. What words can you use to describe them? **List as many adjectives as you can which tell something about these nouns. We have started each list for you.**

Path	Actor
1. worn	1. skilled
2. familiar	2. friendly
3.	3.
4.	4.
5.	5.
6.	6.
7.	7.
8.	8.

95

▶ **Here are the eight vocabulary words for this lesson:**

comic	degree	education	guide
value	earned	path	concerned

▶ **There are four blank spaces in the story below. Four vocabulary words have already been used in the story. They are underlined. Use the other four words to fill in the blank spaces.**

People who can make other people laugh have a special gift. One of these gifted people is Bill Cosby, the comic. But Bill tries to mix laughter with _____ . Bill's family knows the value of learning. Without it, your chances for success are poor.

Bill was a student, even while in the Navy. He _____ his high school diploma by taking courses through the mail. When one has to work and study at the same time, the path to success is not easy. But Bill kept at it. He became a great success. Yet, there was one more college _____ that Bill wanted. He wanted to prepare himself to guide kids. He was _____ about the number of kids who drop out of school. So he studied as a part-time student at the University of Massachusetts for seven years. Finally, he made it. At the age of 39, he could honestly be called "Doctor."

▶ **On a separate sheet of paper or in your notebook, do any one or more of the exercises below for extra credit. Then turn them in to your teacher.**

1 If Bill Cosby is one of your favorite comics, tell why he makes you laugh. Write a short paragraph explaining why he is so funny or how he is different from other comics. Or write about another comic and explain why he or she is your favorite.

2 Many people decide to go back to school while they have jobs. Do you think it is hard to go to school and work at the same time? Why?

3 *Sesame Street* and *The Electric Company* are two television shows that have helped children learn to read. If you have seen either of these shows, write a short paragraph telling what you saw. Do you think these programs help children learn to read?

The brontosaur had been feeding on plants nearly all day. Suddenly, it heard a noise. An allosaur appeared at the edge of the water. Hooked claws buried themselves in the skin of the brontosaur. The brontosaur tried to move into deeper water. But its legs were so heavy, it moved slowly. The allosaur sank its sharp teeth into the backbone of the brontosaur. The brontosaur tried to fight back. But its mouth was small and its teeth were weak. Finally, the fatal battle was over. The allosaur started to feed on the brontosaur. Then it returned to the jungle.

The brontosaur and the allosaur were dinosaurs. Brontosaur was one of the largest. The brontosaur was 70 feet long. That is twice as long as most classrooms! And this dinosaur weighed about 35 tons. It would take ten elephants to weigh as much as one brontosaur!

The allosaur was the principal enemy of the brontosaur. Although it was half the size of the brontosaur, it was a powerful and skillful hunter. The allosaur terrified other dinosaurs.

There are no dinosaurs on earth today. The roar of these monsters is gone. But millions of years ago the land, sea, and sky were filled with dinosaurs.

MAKE A LIST

▶ **There are eight vocabulary words in this lesson. In the story, they are boxed in color. Copy the vocabulary words here.**

1. _____
2. _____
3. _____
4. _____

5. _____
6. _____
7. _____
8. _____

▶ Here are the eight words you copied on the previous page. Write them in alphabetical order in the blank spaces below.

fatal	monsters	dinosaurs	tons
claws	terrified	powerful	principal

1. _____   5. _____

2. _____   6. _____

3. _____   7. _____

4. _____   8. _____

~~~~~~~ WHAT DO THE WORDS MEAN? ~~~~~~~

▶ Here are some meanings for the eight vocabulary words in this lesson. Four words have been written beside their meanings. Write the other four words next to their meanings.

1. _____dinosaurs_____ large lizardlike animals that lived millions of years ago

2. _____principal_____ main; most important

3. _____ very frightened; scared

4. _____ sharp, curved nails on foot of an animal or bird

5. _____tons_____ measures of weight

6. _____ large, scary animals; huge beasts

7. _____powerful_____ very strong; mighty

8. _____ deadly; causing death

wwwwwwwwww USE YOUR OWN WORDS wwwwwwwwww

▶ Look at the picture. What words come into your mind? Write them on the blank lines below. To help you get started, here are two good words:

1. _____swamp_____ 5. _____

2. _____fight_____ 6. _____

3. _____ 7. _____

4. _____ 8. _____

101

▶ A **synonym** is a word that means the same, or nearly the same, as another word. *Happy* and *glad* are synonyms.

▶ The column on the left contains the eight key words in the story. To the right of each key word are three other words or groups of words. Two of these are synonyms for the key word. Circle the two synonyms.

1. fatal	deadly	wounded	causing death
2. monsters	birds	large beasts	huge animals
3. dinosaurs	lizardlike creatures	anything old	prehistoric animals
4. tons	measures of weight	amounts of 2,000 pounds	measures of height
5. claws	hooks	sharp nails	clues
6. terrified	friendly	frightened	scared
7. powerful	very strong	graceful	mighty
8. principal	priceless	main	most important

An **adjective** is a word that describes or tells about persons, things, or places. The underlined words in the following sentences are adjectives.

The <u>old</u>, <u>green</u> house belongs to the <u>new</u> mayor.

▶ **Underline the adjectives in the following sentences. The first one has been done for you.**

1. The <u>powerful</u> roar of these <u>tremendous</u> monsters would scare their <u>weak</u> enemies.

2. The deadly battle was over in ten minutes.

3. The allosaur was a clever, skillful hunter.

4. The terrible monster crawled out of the dark, damp swamp.

5. The allosaur had hooked claws and sharp teeth.

6. Although the bronotosaur was immense, it had a small mouth.

7. These strange animals lived many centuries ago.

8. With a final roar, the brontosaur retreated to safe territory.

▶ Here are the eight vocabulary words for this lesson:

dinosaurs	monsters	principal	powerful
claws	terrified	tons	fatal

▶ There are four blank spaces in the story below. Four vocabulary words have already been used in the story. They are underlined. Use the other four words to fill in the blank spaces.

The "Time Machine" can take you back to the age of <u>dinosaurs</u>. You walk carefully through swamplike land. You hear a terrible roar. There, in the center of the jungle, two <u>monsters</u> are fighting for their lives. It will be a _____ battle. Only one can come out alive. You are the first person to see a struggle between a brontosaur and an allosaur. The size of the monsters amazes you. They must weigh many

_____ . The allosaur is the <u>principal</u> enemy of the brontosaur. It moves quickly. Its

_____ dig deeply into the skin of its enemy. Its powerful teeth grip the neck of the brontosaur. The <u>fatal</u> battle is soon over. The allosaur lifts its head and gives a cry of victory. The other dinosaurs are

_____ of the allosaur. They run from the sound of battle. They want no part of this fight.

▶ **On a separate sheet of paper or in your notebook, do any one or more of the exercises below for extra credit. Then turn them in to your teacher.**

1 In the story a brontosaur and an allosaur are mentioned. These were the names of two types of dinosaurs. There were many others. See how many kinds of dinosaurs you can name. Any book on dinosaurs should give you the names of at least three more. Some dictionaries may also give you names.

2 Imagine you are living in the days of the dinosaurs. Describe how you would protect yourself against an allosaur who has decided to look for food near your cave. List what weapons you would use and describe your plan to defeat the monster.

3 Dinosaurs were large, four-limbed reptiles or lizards who roamed our land millions of years ago. Some walked on their hind legs; others on all fours. Some were flesh eaters; others were plant eaters. See how much information you can supply about the life and death of a dinosaur. Your librarian should be able to help you with this.

When Beverly Sills was only three, she sang on radio. At six she won an amateur hour prize.

Everyone called her Bubbles because of her warm personality. She became one of the greatest opera stars in the world. She sang at the Metropolitan Opera in New York, the home of great voices.

Beverly trained long and hard. For ten years she trudged from office to office, trying to get a job. She was eager to try for any part. Her talent brought her to the New York City Opera. She did so well in the opera *Julius Caesar* that she was given star billing. One critic wrote, "If I were recommending the wonders of New York City, I'd place Beverly Sills at the top of the list."

But Beverly was not only a great singer. She was also a fine actor. Her interpretation of operatic roles moved audiences to tears or wild applause. She could perform roles in 90 operas. After leaving the operatic stage, she became director of the New York City Opera.

She has also known tragedy. Her children were born handicapped. Her daughter is almost completely deaf. Her son is retarded. Beverly stopped singing for a time to help her children. When Beverly returned to opera she was a different singer. She felt she could tackle any role.

Today Beverly Sills is one of the opera world's best known celebrities. Opera lovers everywhere salute her.

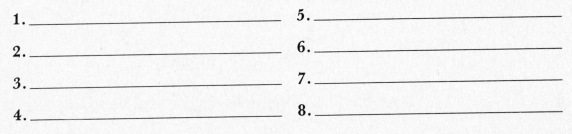

~~~~~~~~~~~~~~~~~~~ MAKE A LIST ~~~~~~~~~~~~~~~~~~~

▶ **There are eight vocabulary words in this lesson. In the story, they are boxed in color. Copy the vocabulary words here.**

1. _____   5. _____

2. _____   6. _____

3. _____   7. _____

4. _____   8. _____

MAKE AN ALPHABETICAL LIST

▶ Here are the eight words you copied on the previous page. Write them in alphabetical order in the blank spaces below.

salute	amateur	trudged	interpretation
eager	handicapped	recommending	opera

1. _____   5. _____

2. _____   6. _____

3. _____   7. _____

4. _____   8. _____

WHAT DO THE WORDS MEAN?

▶ Here are some meanings for the eight vocabulary words in this lesson. Four words have been written beside their meanings. Write the other four words next to their meanings.

1. _____opera_____ story that is set to music and sung

2. _____ praise; hold in high regard

3. _____recommending_____ suggesting; advising

4. _____ physically or mentally disabled; crippled

5. _____ not professional; done for pleasure

6. _____trudged_____ walked in a tired way; walked slowly and with effort

7. _____ anxious; wanting something very much

8. _____interpretation_____ the way one delivers a song; bringing out the meaning of a song

▶ Look at the picture. What words come into your mind? Write them on the blank lines below. To help you get started, here are two good words:

1. _____singer_____   5. _____

2. _____costume_____   6. _____

3. _____   7. _____

4. _____   8. _____

109

▶ A **synonym** is a word that means the same, or nearly the same, as another word. *Happy* and *glad* are synonyms.

▶ The column on the left contains the eight key words in the story. To the right of each key word are three other words or groups of words. Two of these are synonyms for the key word. Circle the two synonyms.

1. **recommending**	advising	denying	suggesting
2. **opera**	singer	story set to music	musical performance
3. **interpretation**	interruption	certain way of singing	special style
4. **trudged**	rode	tramped	walked in a tired way
5. **handicapped**	healthy	crippled	unable to function normally
6. **eager**	wanting very much	early	anxious
7. **amateur**	done for fun	not professional	original
8. **salute**	sing	honor	praise

110

▶ In each of the following sentences there are words which require capital letters. Rewrite each sentence so the words are correctly capitalized. Remember that capital letters are used in the following places: first word in a sentence; names of people, cars, cities, states, countries; days of the week; months of the year. The first one has been done for you.

1. one of beverly sills's favorite roles was that of cleopatra.

One of Beverly Sills's favorite roles was that of Cleopatra.

_____

_____

2. a major goal of opera singers is to appear at the metropolitan opera in new york city.

_____

_____

_____

3. another opera that beverly sills has sung in is *norma*.

_____

_____

_____

4. another famous opera house is la scala in milan, italy.

_____

_____

_____

5. beverly sills is brooklyn's gift to the metropolitan opera.

_____

_____

_____

▶ Here are the eight vocabulary words for this lesson:

handicapped	opera	salute	recommending
interpretation	eager	amateur	trudged

▶ There are four blank spaces in the story below. Four vocabulary words have already been used in the story. They are underlined. Use the other four words to fill in the blank spaces.

Opera stars are among the most interesting people in the world. Beverly Sills was one of the most exciting. Beverly was not only a great singer, but she was also a great actress.

She began singing almost before she could walk. She sang as an _____ every chance she got. She practiced for years. She trudged the streets of New York trying to get a break. Finally she got a chance to sing with the New York City Opera. Her _____ of Cleopatra made her a star. Soon, eager crowds were standing in line waiting to hear Beverly sing. Then Beverly had to give up her career for a time. She had to help her two _____ children. But she returned to the opera. And she became an even better singer than before.

When recommending the joys of opera to your friends, be sure to include a _____ to Beverly Sills.

▶ **On a separate sheet of paper or in your notebook, do any one or more of the exercises below for extra credit. Then turn them in to your teacher.**

1 Of all the stories you have read or seen on television, which is the one story you would like to see as an opera? Name your story. Tell why you would like to see it performed as an opera.

2 All kinds of music are performed in the world today. What kind of music do you like to listen to? Who is your favorite singer? Write two or three sentences telling why.

3 Many people love opera and have recordings of famous operas. See if you can find a record of an opera. You might be able to borrow it from the library. Then play it at home. What do you like about it? What don't you like? Write two or three sentences explaining your likes and dislikes.

A DOLPHIN PERFORMS

The people scramble to their seats. The show is about to begin! The dolphin's trainer stands high above the water. The dolphin leaps. It grabs a fish from the trainer's hand. Then it **plunges** back into the tank.

Thousands of years ago, the dolphin's ancestors lived on land. Today, the dolphin lives in the sea. Dolphins are often confused with porpoises. The dolphin has a pointed nose, mouth, and jaw. The porpoise has a rounded head. The dolphin has a slender, hairless body. The porpoise has a **stocky** body.

Dolphins are **excellent** swimmers. Although they have no back **limbs**, they have strong tails. These tails help dolphins swim as fast as 25 miles an hour.

The dolphin is one of the most **intelligent** animals in the world. Dolphins can imitate things. They can **memorize**, too. That is how they can be trained to do tricks.

But that isn't all. Dolphins make many clicking and whistling sounds. Some scientists believe that the sounds are a form of language. The echoes of the clicks help dolphins find food. The whistles help dolphins **communicate** with one another. Someday people may learn how to communicate with these friendly animals.

MAKE A LIST

▶ There are eight vocabulary words in this lesson. In the story, they are boxed in color. Copy the vocabulary words here.

1. _scramble_   5. _limbs_

2. _____   6. _intelligent_

3. _stocky_   7. _memorize_

4. _excellent_   8. _communicate_

▶ Here are the eight words you copied on the previous page. Write them in alphabetical order in the blank spaces below.

excellent	stocky	plunges	limbs
memorize	communicate	intelligent	scramble

1. _____   5. _____

2. _____   6. _____

3. _____   7. _____

4. _____   8. _____

~~~~~~~ WHAT DO THE WORDS MEAN? ~~~~~~~

▶ Here are some meanings for the eight vocabulary words in this lesson. Four words have been written beside their meanings. Write the other four words next to their meanings.

1. _____excellent_____ very good; better than others

2. _____ heavily built; thick and strong

3. _____ dives; jumps in

4. _____limbs_____ arms or legs; parts extending from body

5. _____ learn by heart; remember

6. _____communicate_____ exchange messages; give information

7. _____ very bright; having much knowledge

8. _____scramble_____ rush; move quickly

116

~~~~~~~~~~~~~~~~~~ USE YOUR OWN WORDS ~~~~~~~~~~~~

▶ Look at the picture. What words come into your mind?
Write them on the blank lines below. To help you get
started, here are two good words:

1._____jump_____   5._____

2._____splash____   6._____

3._____   7._____

4._____   8._____

~~~~~~~~~~~~~   ~~~~~~~~~~~~

▶ A **synonym** is a word that means the same, or nearly the same, as another word. *Happy* and *glad* are synonyms.

▶ The column on the left contains the eight key words in the story. To the right of each key word are three other words or groups of words. Two of these are synonyms for the key word. Circle the two synonyms.

1. **communicate**   exchange ideas   (talk)   refuse

2. **limbs**   (arms)   bodies   legs

3. **stocky**   short   (thick)   slim

4. **scramble**   (rush)   scribble   move quickly

5. **plunges**   fills   (dives)   jumps in

6. **memorize**   understand   (remember)   learn by heart

7. **excellent**   very fine   (very good)   modest

8. **intelligent**   (smart)   pleasant   brainy

▶ Many words end in *ed, er* or *ing*. These endings can change the meaning of a word or form a new word. **Add the right ending to the word before each sentence. Then write the new word in the blank space. Remember, sometimes you drop the final *e* before adding the ending. The first one has been done for you.**

1. **memorize**   The dolphin <u>memorized</u> many new tricks.

2. **scramble**   Alice and Diane were late and <u>ScramBle</u> to their seats.

3. **plunge**   Several porpoises <u>plunge</u> into the large tank.

4. **train**   She is the best <u>train</u> dolphin we ever had here.

5. **communicate**   When the dolphins whistle, they are <u>Communicate</u> with one another.

6. **help**   The <u>Help</u> began to feed the dolphin.

7. **whistle**   Lee thought we could learn to talk to dolphins by <u>Whistle</u> and clicking.

8. **perform**   The dolphin is a star <u>Performer</u>.

119

▶ Here are the eight vocabulary words for this lesson:

scramble	communicate	plunges	stocky
intelligent	memorize	excellent	limbs

▶ There are four blank spaces in the story below. Four vocabulary words have already been used in the story. They are underlined. Use the other four words to fill in the blank spaces.

We are going on vacation next week. Our family has decided to return to Sea World. We want to see the dolphins perform. This time it might not be so crowded. We won't have to ___scramble___ for seats. I hope we won't have to risk our limbs to see. The dolphins are our favorites. These intelligent animals seem to know how to ___communicate___ with their trainer. They have the ability to memorize many tricks. My favorite trick is when a dolphin ___plunges___ into the water and comes up wearing a life preserver.

Some people get dolphins mixed up with porpoises. Both are excellent swimmers, but the porpoise has a ___stocky___ body. More important, the dolphin is smarter and seems to enjoy performing. Dolphins are born actors.

120

▶ **On a separate sheet of paper or in your notebook, do any one or more of the exercises below for extra credit. Then turn them in to your teacher.**

1 Perhaps you have seen dolphins on TV or in live water shows. They usually are the star performers. Can you describe some of the clever tricks they do? Which trick is your favorite?

2 Imagine you found a dolphin who could communicate with you. What three questions would you ask this intelligent animal? Remember, you can only ask three questions—and you want to learn as much as you can.

3 The story tells us that "the dolphin is one of the most intelligent animals in the world." Try to name three other animals which are considered to be very intelligent. Which is your choice for the most intelligent? Tell why.

A

amateur *[AM uh chur]* not professional; done for pleasure, not money

ambitious *[am BISH us]* wanting fame or success

ancestor *[AN ses tur]* great-grandparent and those who came before

ancient *[AYN shunt]* belonging to times long past; very old

applaud *[uh PLAWD]* to clap one's hands together (to show enjoyment or respect)

attracted *[uh TRAK ted]* gathered; brought together

author *[AW thur]* writer

autograph *[AWT uh graf]* hand-written name; signature, especially of a famous person

B

beat *[BEET]* rhythm of a piece of music

beneath *[bee NEETH]* below; underneath

brand *[BRAND]* to make a mark on the skin with a hot iron

C

capable *[KAY puh bul]* able to do

capturing *[KAP chur]* winning; gaining control of

chart *[CHAHRT]* diagram; map or graph

chunk *[CHUNGK]* a short, thick piece; good-sized portion

claws *[KLAWZ]* sharp, curved nails on foot of an animal or bird

combat *[kum BAT]* to fight or work against; try to get rid of

comic *[KOM ik]* a person who makes you laugh

communicate *[kuh MYOO nuh kayt]* exchange messages; give information

compact *[kum PAKT]* taking up little space; solidly packed

companion *[kum PAN yun]* friend; pal

compass *[KUM puhs]* instrument used to tell directions

concerned *[kon SURND]* interested in someone or something

confidence *[KON fuh duns]* having faith or trust in oneself

connection *[kuh NEK shun]* link

conservation *[kon sur VAY shun]* protection

critical *[KRIT ih kul]* disapproving; not supportive

D

defect *[DEE fekt]* weakness; disability

degree *[duh GREE]* a paper or diploma showing someone has graduated, usually from college

demonstrated *[DEM un strayt id]* showed, proved

descendants *[dee SEN dunts]* people born of a certain family; heirs

desire *[duh ZYR]* wish; purpose

difficult *[DIF ih kult]* not easy; hard

dinosaurs *[DY nuh sorz]* large lizardlike animals that lived millions of years ago

discover *[dis KUV ur]* find out; uncover

display *[dis PLAY]* demonstration

donated *[DOH nayt id]* gave

driven *[DRIV un]* ambitious; filled with the need to succeed

dull *[DULL]* not interesting; boring

E

eager *[EE gur]* anxious; wanting something very much

earned *[URND]* gained as a result of hard work; acquired

education *[ej yoo KAY shun]* the process of learning; gained knowledge

essence *[ES uns]* basic character

established *[es TAB lisht]* set up; founded

estimated *[ES tuh mayt id]* guessed at the size or value of something

excellent *[EK suh lunt]* very good; better than others

expense *[ek SPENS]* cost

extraordinary *[ek STROR duh nehr ee]* very unusual

F

fatal *[FAYT ul]* deadly; causing death

future *[FYOO chur]* a time to come; what is ahead

generous *[JEN ur us]* willing to share

glacier *[GLAY sheer]* extremely large mass of ice and snow

great *[GRAYT]* much above average

guide *[GYD]* direct; show the way

H

handicapped *[HAN dee kapt]* physically or mentally disabled; crippled

hike *[HYK]* take a long walk or march

horrible *[HOR uh bul]* terrible; frightful

I

iceberg *[EYES burg]* mountain of ice; large chunk of ice broken off from a glacier

immense *[ih MENS]* huge; very large

informed *[in FORMD]* given information; told

injury *[IN juh ree]* a wound or damage

injustice *[in JUS tis]* something that harms the rights of others

institution *[in stuh TOO shun]* building housing an organization

intelligent *[in TEL ih jent]* very bright; having much knowledge

interfere *[in tur FEER]* to get in the way of

interpretation *[in tur pruh TAY shun]* the way one delivers a song; bringing out the meaning of a song

invested *[in VEST id]* put money into

J

jarred *[JAHRD]* shaken; jolted

L

limbs *[LIMZ]* arms or legs; parts extending from body

literally *[LIT ur ul ee]* actually

local *[LOH kul]* of a small area; regional

M

mayor *[MAY ur]* the head of a city

memorize *[MEM uh ryz]* learn by heart; remember

mentioned *[MEN shund]* introduced

modern *[MOD urn]* new; up-to-date

monsters *[MON sturz]* large, scary animals; huge beasts

N

nation *[NAY shun]* a country

O

observation *[ob zur VAY shun]* attention; watching

opera *[OP ruh]* story that is set to music and sung

operator *[OP uh RAYT ur]* a person who runs a machine

opportunity *[op ur TOO nuh tee]* a chance, usually a good one

P

path *[PATH]* a road or track

pep *[PEP]* energy; liveliness; spirit

perform *[pur FORM]* do; act

planets *[PLAN itz]* any of the nine heavenly bodies that orbit the sun

pledged *[PLEJD]* made a strong promise

plunges *[PLUNJ ez]* dives; jumps in

powerful *[POW ur ful]* very strong; mighty

prevents *[pri VENTZ]* stops; keeps something from happening

principal *[PRIN suh pul]* main; most important

properly *[PROP ur lee]* correctly; without mistakes

publisher *[PUB lish ur]* maker of printed books

Q

quality *[KWAHL uh ti]* of obvious excellence

R

race *[RAYCE]* a contest, often for a job in government

realistic *[ree uh LIS tik]* true, correct

reared *[REERD]* stood on hind legs; done by a horse

recommended *[rek uh MEND id]* suggested; advised

remove *[ree MOOV]* take off; take away

reporter *[ree POR tur]* someone who writes about or tells about the news

reviewers *[rih VYOO urz]* people who tell about new films

riot *[RY ut]* a wild disturbance caused by a group of people

rodeo *[ROH dee oh]* a public show for the skills of cowboys and cowgirls

S

saddle *[SAD ul]* leather seat for a rider on horseback

salute *[suh LOOT]* praise; hold in high regard

scramble *[SKRAM bul]* rush; move quickly

separated *[SEP uh rayt id]* apart; not together

series *[SEER eez]* TV show that appears each week

staggering *[STAG ur ing]* overwhelming

stocky *[STOK ee]* heavily built; thick and strong

struggle *[STRUG ul]* work hard for

superstition *[soo pur STISH un]* belief based on ignorance and fear

syndrome *[SIN drohm]* group of characteristics, or symptoms, indicating a condition

T

terrified *[TER uh fyd]* very frightened; scared

tons *[TUNZ]* measures of weight (one ton equals 2,000 pounds)

traced *[TRAYSD]* followed; tracked

trudged *[TRUJD]* walked in a tired way; walked slowly and with effort

U

university *[yoo nuh VUR suh tee]* a school of higher learning; college

V

value *[VAL yoo]* the worth of something

visible *[VIS uh bul]* can be seen; can be observed

W

wit *[WIT]* humor; intelligence